Favourite Fables
from
La Fontaine

Favourite Fables from La Fontaine

Translated by John Orpen

Illustrated by Benvenuti

HAMLYN
London · New York · Sydney · Toronto

Published 1972 by
THE HAMLYN PUBLISHING GROUP LIMITED
London·New York·Sydney·Toronto
Hamlyn House, Feltham, Middlesex, England

© Copyright this edition, The Hamlyn Publishing Group Limited 1972
© Copyright 1971 by Editions des Deux Coqs d'Or, Paris
    and Mondadori–OGAM, Verona

Printed by Officine Grafiche Arnoldo Mondadori, Verona, Italy
ISBN 0 600 33472 4

FOREWORD

The lives of animals are governed by the laws of Nature—laws which are un-influenced by either sentiment or prejudice. Animals, of course, have none of humanity's vices, but neither do they have our sense of humour.

However, La Fontaine's animals are rather different. He has given them human voices and human characteristics—and not always the best of these either!

So you must remember when you're reading these fables that his animals are really actors, playing the part of men and women, with all the good and bad traits of ordinary people.

In this book you'll meet the animal-actors of La Fontaine's fields and forests and streams, counterparts of people we all know—bustling, busybody Mrs Fly, crafty Captain Fox, sly Mrs Weasel and helpful Doctor Cormorant.

All have the characteristics of people you'll meet in real life one day or other—some of them you may even have met already!

La Fontaine's original text was written in seventeenth century French verse, but since his Fables deal with universal themes, they have a strength of their own, and whatever language frontiers they have to cross, they remain essentially La Fontaine.

John Orpen

CONTENTS

THE DONKEY AND THE LITTLE DOG

We should never try our luck too far—disaster can so easily result. Heavy-footed, clumsy people don't make the best of dancers, and few of us have so much natural grace that we'll please everyone.

So if that's not our sort of life it's best to do the job we can and not be like the donkey in my tale, who thought he should be treated like a lap dog.

'Why should this little snuffling dog be such a play-thing, when all I get are kicks and blows? What does it do to merit such soft treatment? It lifts a paw—and they adore his clever ways! So all I need to do is just the same!'

And so he came into the house to imitate the little dog, trotted to his master's chair and laid affectionate hooves right in his lap. They were really very heavy, and certainly rather smelly!

To be quite sure that everyone could understand what he was trying to say, the donkey loudly brayed in friendly greeting.

'Lord, what an awful noise!', exclaimed his master. 'Take your great hooves off, you brute!'.

The outcry brought the stable lad inside the house at once, to drive the donkey back to work with whip and boot.

THE DONKEY IN THE LION'S SKIN

A donkey wrapped himself inside a lion's skin, and for a while took everybody in. Such fun to frighten everyone, the donkey thought. But then one day one of his huge ears popped out from his disguise and the Constable soon tumbled to the donkey's trick. But no one else saw through it then. All they could see was that the Constable was chasing after King Lion—and armed with nothing but a stick!

They soon realized the truth, and so should we when we meet someone like that donkey. Outside he may be frightening and terrible, but underneath the fierce disguise, he's peaceable and quite amenable.

THE ANIMALS AND THE PLAGUE

Once, long ago, the creatures of the world tried their Creator's patience much too far and the dreaded plague appeared. Thousands died, tens of thousands more became so weak they had no strength to fight, or even eat. The foxes and the wolves allowed their prey to get away and even the gentle doves fled from each other. Love and hope both vanished from the earth.

The Lion then called a Council and said: 'Friends, I'm sure this dreadful thing has come about because we're guilty of some awful crime. Let the most guilty one among us sacrifice himself to end the plague. He may absolve us all from further horror. We know from history that such a sacrifice may work a miracle again. Come, let us all speak honestly and see what can be done. As to my part, I confess that I have often given way to my voracious appetite and bolted innocent sheep. What harm had they done me? Why, none at all. But worse, sometimes I ate the shepherd, too! So be it—I will sacrifice myself if no one has worse crimes to tell. Let each of us, as I have done, make a clean breast of it, for true justice will demand that the most guilty of us all should perish.'

'Sire,' spoke the fox, 'you are too good a King of Beasts. Your scruples make of you a far too gentle judge. Why shed your tears over some sheep, such lowly animals? Is it a crime to eat their flesh? I'd say by eating them you do them honour! As for a shepherd (or two) nothing is too bad for them, seeing that they hold dominion over animals.'

Flatterers applauded the cunning fox's speech. Well, we can't push analogies too far, so better not enquire too closely into the conduct of fierce creatures like the tiger, or the bear, or others of their kind. All these were given the benefit of doubt, some even praised for doing their duty, like the humble jackal.

When everyone had said their mind, it was the donkey's turn.

'Once, years ago, I strayed into a pleasant field belonging to some monks, I felt so hungry and the grass was so inviting, I was tempted to crop some of it. It was wrong of me to yield, I know, but there it is.'

His speech raised loud and instant protest—how shocked the assembled Council was!

A wolf, with some pretensions to the law, cried angrily above the din that: 'Here was the cause of all our ills!'

All judged the donkey the most guilty and called for instant hanging. And this was done.

The moral—mark it well—is this: all courts are prone to prejudice, and, if you're weak, they'll not relent, but judge the strong the innocent.

THE DONKEY CARRYING SALT AND THE DONKEY CARRYING SPONGES

Looking like a Roman Emperor urging on his troops, a donkey driver waved his charges forward faster still. One of the two was loaded with heavy bags of salt, the other trotted lightly with his load of sponges.

Up hill and down the convoy went until it was stopped by a stream, which gave some trouble to the donkeys. But the driver often came this way and knew his route—or so he thought! Jumping on to the back of the donkey with the sponges, into the stream he plunges, driving the salt-laden ass on in front of them.

This one was very keen to reach the other side but in his haste fell into a hole in the bed of the stream, bobbing up and down in clouds of spray. He plunged about so much that all the salt was washed away! How light his load felt now!

The donkey with the sponges, seeing his stable-mate so far in front made greater efforts still but only sank up to his neck, drenching himself, his master and his load, which soaked up water and became as heavy as a sack of stones! Down sank the donkey, while his master hastily prepared to drown.

Someone rescued that frightened pair, but not before they'd all three learned that water's not the same as air!

THE MILLER, HIS SON AND
THEIR DONKEY

A miller and his son, a stripling of fifteen, decided they would sell
their donkey at the nearest Fair. To be sure the moke arrived quite
fit and worthy to be sold they tied his legs together and carried
him along slung underneath a pole.

A silly pair they must have looked, carrying a donkey upside
down!

The first to see them staggering along burst out laughing:
'What's this new game you're playing? I'll tell you this—the
silliest donkey of you lot isn't the one that's got four legs!'

The miller blushed at these remarks and secretly admitted he was really rather stupid, so they untied the donkey's legs and made him walk. The donkey brayed in protest—he'd quite enjoyed being carried.

The miller ignored the noise and told his son to get on its back while he followed on foot.

They met three merchants next, who found the miller's plan quite shocking. The eldest of the three cried to the lad: 'Hey, you! Get off and let the old man ride—you're young enough to use your own two feet!'

'Gentlemen,' the miller said, 'we'll do just as you say.' The boy got down, and the miller (who was rather short of breath by now) climbed on its back and on they went again.

Then a group of giggling girls came by and one said: 'What a shame to see that poor lad hobbling past, while that old man, who ought to lose a bit of weight, slumps on his donkey's groaning back.'

'Well, fat or not,' the miller cried, 'I'm the eldest of the three and have priority, so mind your own affairs, my girl!' But after lots of repartee, the miller did at last agree he might be wrong. He let his son get up on the donkey's back as well, and the two of them rode on again.

They hadn't gone a yard before another group of people found some other thing to criticize. One said: 'These two are mad—just fancy loading that poor donkey with the two of them at once! Have they no pity for their poor old moke? I suppose that, if they ever reach the Fair, they'll sell his hide; no more, because that's all there will be left to sell!'

'My goodness,' growled the miller, 'it's impossible to please these people—but just once more we'll try!'

So down they got again and went on foot, the donkey trotting out ahead, well pleased at being relieved of such a heavy load.

Another passer-by saw fit to say: 'Well, I never knew it was the thing to do to let one's donkey trot ahead, not even burdened with a saddle, while his master puffs along behind? They ought to wrap him up in cotton wool if he's so precious! Silly people—wearing out their shoes while their beast of burden skips along at ease!'

After hearing these remarks, the miller swore he'd had enough. 'All right,' he fumed, 'if you all say I'm stupid as a donkey, I'll admit it—but from this minute on, and whether people praise or blame me, whether they say this or that or nothing, I shall do exactly as I please!'

How wise he was to take his own advice.

THE CAT AND THE WISE OLD RAT

There was another story-teller (I forget his name) who
wrote about a cat who slaughtered rats and mice at
such a rate he put the Goths to shame. The poor
things had no peace at all, and their short lives
became a misery.

This tyrant among cats became so widely known it
was even said his great ambition was to rid the world
of all its rats and mice for ever.

Now, they were used to traps with balanced planks, and poison-bait, and those nasty little springs which broke their backs, but this one cat was worse than all these dangers put together. There came a time when they no longer dared to peer out from their holes for fear of instant seizure. And so, of course, the cat caught none of them and became extremely hungry—and therefore still more cunning!

He then pretended to be dead and hung by his back legs down from a beam. The mice and rats peeped out at this strange sight and felt they guessed the reason. Their enemy the cat had got so hungry he'd been stealing meat or else he'd scratched someone important, or thieved a fine, ripe cheese. But anyway they'd hanged him up for dead!

Lots of merrymaking then went on and from their holes, a little timidly at first, they finally emerged, then shot back to their holes again, just to make sure it wasn't yet another trap. But the cat kept absolutely still, so out they came completely, sure that their great enemy was dead at last.

But suddenly it all went wrong—the 'dead' cat sprang alive, slipped the knot from round his feet, and seized the nearest ones in steel-sharp claws.

'I know a trick or two,' he cried. 'That was an old ruse and I'll tell you this—your holes won't save you—sooner or later I'll get you all!'

He knew their memories were short and later on adopted yet a new disguise, coating himself in flour and crouching in an empty bin. It was a simple trick and like all simple tricks it worked.

The ever-curious mice and rats came sniffing round this quite unusual bait.

But one old stager of a rat,
knowing a trick or two as well as cats, who'd even
lost his tail in fights, kept well away.

'That lump of whitened something isn't right—if I
were you I'd keep away from it,' he warned the
others. Then he guessed it was the cat and cried to it:
'I smell some trick and even if they'd tied you in a
sack of flour, I'd keep away from you!'

Seasoned campaigners don't forget past lessons.
As he scurried away he summed them up in just two
words: 'Safety First!'

THE WEASEL, THE RABBIT AND THE WISE OLD CAT

Early one fine morning the rabbit left his home to skip
and tumble on the soft, thyme-scented grass. But when
he got back he had a dreadful shock—old Mrs Weasel
had moved in, and with all her belongings as well!

'Oh no!' the rabbit cried. 'Mrs Weasel, you
must go at once, or I shall make an awful fuss!'

But Mrs Weasel merely smiled with all her fine, sharp teeth, and looked down her long, thin nose.

'Certainly not,' she said, 'as everyone knows, possession's nine-tenths of the law. And I'm here now, as you can see. Anyway, to get in here, one's got to crawl on all fours—if this had been some splendid castle, we'd have had cause to fight!'

'Custom and usage, Ma'am, have made that burrow mine,' tearfully answered the rabbit, 'and it came to me through all my family—it's my inheritance!'

'Oh, very well,' sighed Mrs Weasel, 'we'll have the case decided by that wise old cat who lives close by.'

The wise old cat lived all alone and yet despite his solitary state he always looked well-fed and sleek. Into his lair the two disputers came and told him all their troubles.

'Come closer, closer, my dear friends—I'm getting old and going a little deaf,' he said.

Closer they came, all unsuspecting, close enough for the cat to grab them both in steely claws!

Now they both pleaded the same cause—to be set free at once! But he ate them both, despite their pleadings. And that's what happens when one brings one's little quarrels to be settled by unscrupulous Kings.

THE CAT AND THE TWO SPARROWS

A very young sparrow shared a home with a kitten. They'd been together since both could crawl. Often, the kitten was teased by the sparrow's tricks and many a tumble, beak versus claw, they had on the floor.

But the kitten was always careful not to unsheathe his claws. The sparrow was not so restrained, but just went on jabbing away with his beak—he couldn't sheathe that very well!—so the cat forgave his friend his blows, sharp though they were.

Between good friends, a little horseplay does no harm and peace was a habit hard to break seeing they'd grown up together. So their games were never serious until one day the sparrow next door flew in and somehow a fight started between the two birds.

The cat jumped in to defend his friend.

'This other sparrow,' said the cat, 'has gone too far. No one insults my friend. If I don't step in now, that fellow from next door will get the better of him.' Into the fight he jumped and swallowed the intruder in a moment. Some feathers flew about and that was that.

'Hum,' mused the cat, licking his lips, 'sparrows taste rather good—in fact, I'd like some more of them.'

You can guess the end—the cat ate up the other, too.

Now, what's the moral here? I'll leave it to you!

THE CAT AND THE RAT

Four curious tenants lived at peace in the trunk of a gnarled old tree—a cat, an owl, a rat and a weasel.

One evening a trapper came and spread his deadly nets all round the bole.

Just before dawn, the cat came sneaking down on velvet paws to go off hunting mice. In the dark, the nets were invisible, and into them she fell. She howled in fear and woke the rat who came to see his mortal enemy filled with despair.

The desperate cat entreated the rat to help her out of the clinging nets: 'Good friend,' she said, 'I've always sought to help you, holding you in high esteem. It's your turn now to save me from these nets. Remember how I've always helped you just as though you were one of us—it makes me proud to think of it. I was on my way to Matins to thank the Lord for good friends such as you, but now I'm faced with mortal danger and my life is in your hands. Bite through the cords with your sharp teeth so I can then escape.'

'That's all very fine,' the rat replied. 'But what reward will I get?'

'I swear an eternal alliance with you and your kind,' cried the cat. 'My teeth and my claws will be yours to command—I'll protect you from each of your enemies.' The rat thought hard for a moment and wavered. The cat went on:

'Why, I know for a start that the owl and the weasel are planning to kill you today!'

'You must take me for a fool,' the rat said, 'to ask me to cut you free—I'm not as silly as that!'

And back he scuttled towards his hole in the tree.

But the weasel was waiting close to the entrance, so the rat climbed higher up the bole for safety—but the owl was waiting for him higher still. There was danger everywhere and he thought it would be wiser to face the lesser danger of them all. Back he scuttled to the cat, still trapped inside the net and chewed through the cords as fast as he could. The cat sprang out, and just as they fled, the trapper came back. They ran for miles until all danger was behind.

Then the cat saw that his new-found friend the rat kept a safe distance from him.

31

'Come now, my brother-in-arms,' said the cat, 'let's shake hands on our friendship. Your mistrust does me no honour. You're treating me as though I were still your enemy. Do you think I have forgotten that, by Heaven's grace and your sharp teeth, I owe my life to you?'

'And I,' replied the rat, 'have not forgotten that it's Nature that decrees that cats should be the enemies of rats. I'll have no faith in any pact thrust on one by necessity—what treaty then could force a cat to pay a debt to any rat?'

THE CAT AND THE FOX

A cat and a fox were on a pilgrimage, but two greater brigands you'd never seen. They were just a couple of thieves, poaching and stealing from every farm on the way, a chicken here, a fat cheese there—living off the land in style.

The road was long and tiring and as they grew more

weary, they grew more bored, so to while away the time they had long discussions on all sorts of things. And when they'd nothing else to talk about, they talked about their neighbours. At length, the fox said to the cat: 'You're always saying you've an answer to everything, but I wonder if you're really better than I in dire emergencies? Remember, I have at least a hundred tricks up my sleeve.'

'Perhaps not better than you are—I've only got one trick, it's true—but it's worth a hundred that you can think up!'

As they were arguing they suddenly heard the baying of hounds and a blast from a hunting horn.

'My friend,' the cat cried, 'now's the time for you to rummage through your bag of tricks and find the one that's going to get you out of this. But as for me, here's my one and only well-tried trick . . .' and the cat sprang up the nearest tree to safety.

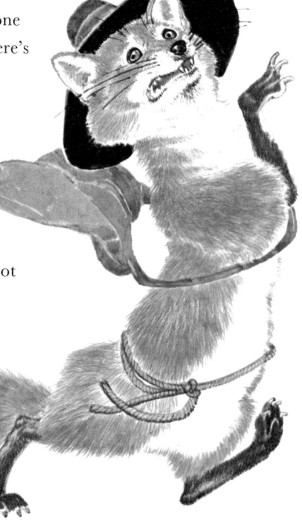

The fox ran here and there, dived down a dozen holes and ran for cover where he could, but all to no avail. They blew smoke down and sent their terriers after him. Out he had to come, into the foxhounds' waiting jaws.

Don't dither like the fox—have one good plan, not fifty or a hundred—when you're in a hurry, you'll find them full of flaws.

THE DONKEY AND THE HORSE

We should always try to help each other, for if
your neighbour drops his load it might fall right
on you. Here's what I mean:

34

A donkey, groaning with a heavy load, was trying to keep up with an arrogant, high-spirited horse.

'Could you not take a little of my load?' the donkey pleaded. 'If not, I'm sure I'll just drop in my tracks. If you could take one of my sacks, it would be such a help.'

The horse just loudly snorted in contempt—he wasn't a beast of burden. The donkey saw it was no use to ask for help from such a blockhead.

He stopped, he swayed, and toppled over, dead.

The horse soon saw the error of his ways. Not only did they put the donkey's sacks on his broad back, but also made him take the donkey's corpse, and under such a weighty double load he very nearly fell as well.

THE HORSE AND THE WOLF

A timber wolf woke from the harshness of the
Winter and saw that it was nearly Spring at last.
The first thing to be done was to replenish his
larder. No sooner had this thought occurred to
him than he saw a horse grazing in a wide green
pasture.

'Now there's a quantity of meat, ten times as
much as on a sheep,' he thought. 'But it's so big,
I'll need to exercize my cunning here—let's sit
and think—yes, I'll be a doctor—where are my
specs?' and off he trotted to the field.

Bowing with respect to the big, strong horse,
the wolf swore he knew a cure for everything,
based naturally on herbs, the simplest, most
effective medicines. With these he'd made a cure
of every ill that Nature sent—so maybe he could
help his equine friend? For to be confined within
this field alone must mean that something wasn't
right with him?

'Well,' said the horse, 'then since you ask, I've
got a sore just underneath my hoof.'

'Ah!' cried the wolf. 'Now that's too bad. We
all need our four limbs and paws—I mean, our
hooves—and many's the horse I've cured of all
his ills quite finally. Just let me have a look,
dear Sir . . .' and down he bent to see.

But his disguise had never fooled the horse, who
lashed out with a hoof, knocking the wolf flying
in a welter of glasses and broken teeth. The wolf

36

got up and ran back to his own patch in the woods, resolved to stalk the prey that Nature fitted him to catch.

THE DOG WHO CHASED SHADOWS

None of us can get things right first time, and lots
of people never do at any time. They ought to
study Aesop's tale about the dog trotting back

home to a meagre dinner when he suddenly saw a fine, fat hare reflected in the placid surface of a stream.

Sure this was his real prey, he plunged in after it, and nearly drowned in the cold, still water.

Somehow he struggled to the bank, half-dead with fright and thoroughly dejected, feeling very stupid to have run after a shadow and let the substance take to flight!

THE DOG WHO ATE HIS MASTER'S DINNER

This sad-eyed dog was sent to get his master's dinner and for greater safety hung it round his neck. He was very tempted to eat the dinner himself but this desire he resisted by trotting faster and faster. Which was very proper of him since all of us are liable to be tempted. It's odd that men can teach a dog restraint and yet they can't restrain themselves.

Faster he trotted the more his resolution weakened. But bigger dogs also run fast and soon a growling mastiff caught up with him and tried to snatch the food from round our hero's neck. The better to protect his cargo, he stopped, laid the precious bundle on the ground between his paws, and flew at his attacker with a will. Soon, all the dogs for miles around were joining in, and being tough scavengers they really made a din.

Our hero couldn't fight them all and since his master's dinner was for certain doomed, he grew determined to at least preserve his share. Above the snarling pack, he boomed: 'Look, friends, let's all stop fighting and each take a piece!'

The fight then stopped, the mob tucked in and everyone had a piece of chicken to himself.

He'd well deserved his portion of the breast— after all, he'd done his very best, and none of us can possibly do more.

THE HEN WHO LAID THE GOLDEN EGGS

In wanting everything greed loses everything.

To illustrate my meaning, there's the story of the hen who, so the old books say, laid a bright, golden egg every day.

Her master couldn't wait to get his hands on more, and sure she was made of solid gold inside, killed her and opened up her carcase—but found her just the same as all the others in his yard.

Having himself destroyed the source of all his wealth, it wasn't any consolation to him to reflect that people when they're greedy over-reach themselves and in a moment lose everything they value, and so become as poor as they had once been rich.

THE COCK AND THE FOX

A wise and experienced old cock was on sentry-go, high in a tree, when a fox came trotting along, bursting with news.

'My friend,' said he in joyful tones, 'a general peace has been declared and I've come specially to tell you all about it. Come down from your high perch and we'll clasp hands in everlasting friendship. But you must hurry—I've twenty miles to run today with this good news. You and yours can go about your lives in peace henceforth. We'll all be brothers—you can light the fires tonight to celebrate. But come on down and let's exchange fraternal greetings!'

'This is the best of news my ears could ever wish to hear,' answered the cock. 'To think that peace shall reign for evermore between us. And my joy is even greater when I hear such news from you, our ancient enemy—ah, look, here come two hounds across the fields—surely bound on the very same errand as you. They run so fast they'll be here soon. I'll come down at once and all four of us shall seal eternal friendship.'

'I must be off,' shouted the fox, 'no time to waste. We'll hold our celebrations by and by—' and off he sprinted like the wind, furious that his clever plan had gone awry.

The wise old cock crowed for an hour with laughter—it's twice the fun to turn the tables on a twister.

THE COCK, THE CAT AND THE VERY YOUNG MOUSE

A very young mouse, with no experience of life, was once nearly caught yet lived to tell this tale:

'Mother,' he said, 'you know the great mountains that encircle our house? I'd climbed to the top and was trotting along like any proud mouse out seeking his fortune when I met two strange-looking animals. One was soft and kindly in manner, gracious in movement. The other was violent in gesture and raucous, too, with a cry that split my ears. On top of his head was an odd piece of flesh, ugly and red, and he'd funny arms he flapped, to jump in the air as though he meant to fly, and he had a long tail that trailed out behind.'

His mother said nothing—her son couldn't know what a cock looked like, nor a cat!

'And then he flapped his arms against his sides and made such a horrible din I fled in a panic. If he hadn't done that I'd have met that other one. He was rather like us, with soft, striped fur and a gentle face with bright and shining eyes. He seemed a charming animal, so much like us in many ways. I was just about to speak to him when that other noisy fiend burst out with all his shrieking and frightened me away.'

'My poor, dear boy,' his mother said, 'that kindly animal you saw who seemed so nice was nothing but a cat whose sleepy air of innocence conceals an age-old tiger's cunning against mice. That other animal, despite his noise, is quite incapable of doing you any harm and more than likely he'll

be killed one day and thrown to us in little bits to
eat. But that cat's diet is almost wholly—us.
Remember in the future when you meet new faces,
never judge them by appearances, however
pleasing they may be!'

47

THE FROGS WHO WANTED A KING

The frogs in the pond had grown weary of
democracy and set up such a croaking and
complaining that Jupiter at last agreed to let them
have their wish—a King. Their Monarch dropped
down from the sky with such a splash the frogs—
easily frightened and terribly jumpy—dived into the
water in a flash, into the reeds, not daring to look
their new King in the face, sure they'd got some
pitiless giant who'd eat them—though it was only
a log the god had thrown them.

King Log's unmoving gravity and air of stiff
solemnity alarmed them all. But one by one, they
crept out from their hiding places, still quaking
from the noise of his arrival, and finally they all

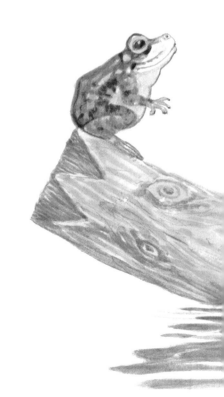

assembled round their silent Monarch, who never moved a muscle. They soon got used to him. Then one of the bolder frogs jumped on His Majesty's broad shoulder. The other frogs all held their breath but King Log never moved nor said a word.

Boredom soon set in—'This King's no good!' the frogs all cried. 'Jupiter—send us a King with life in him!'

The god obliged and sent a silent, long-beaked crane who chased them without mercy and ate up every one he caught. Loudly, the frogs again complained to Jupiter, who said: 'You should have been content with your first form of government, but since you made such loud lament, I gave you what you wanted—a strong and active King. And with the fierce one you've got now, you'll have to be content, for fear of getting worse!'

THE FROG AND THE OX

There was a frog, not much bigger than a hen's egg, who became envious of the majestic size of her neighbour, Lord Ox.

So she puffed and puffed and swelled up, until she was twice as big as her sister.

'Is that enough?' she asked. 'Am I as big as Lord Ox, now?'

'Nothing like it!' cried her sister. 'You're not even as big as his hoof yet—you'll have to swell up a hundred times more, at least!'

So the frog swelled up still more, and more, and just that little bit more until—like a balloon when you stick a pin into it—she burst.

Which was sad, because her sister was just going to say to her: 'You'll never do it—we frogs should know our place.'

THE ANT AND THE GRASSHOPPER

All through the long Summer's heat the grasshopper sang, so when Winter had chased the sun from the sky, she still had no food in her larder—not a single worm, not even a fly.

Well muffled up, clutching her cherished guitar, she hopped to her neighbour's door:

'Dear Mrs Ant, can you spare me some food from your store, till the Spring? Really, I'll pay it all back, and more.'

But old Mrs Ant looked stern:

'What stopped you from putting some by in the fine, warm, golden days?'

'Why, didn't you hear my song? I sang, all through the Summer's haze—'

'Ah,' said the Ant, 'so you sang in the sun, while we worked all day? Well, now you must dance all Winter long—it will keep the cold at bay!'

THE COACH AND THE BUSYBODY FLY

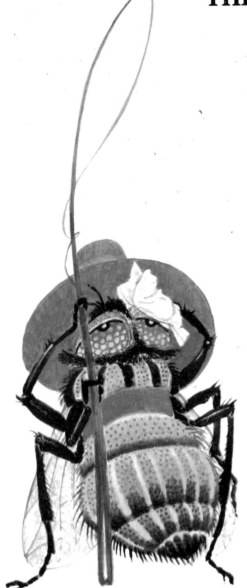

Up a steep and slippery mountain road, burning in the midday sun, six powerful horses strained to pull a heavy coach, loaded with people. But soon it had to stop, the horses spent, with no strength left to pull another foot. Out got the passengers to lighten it, and while the horses rested, along came a busybody fly.

One quick look's enough for her—she sizes up the trouble and decides to help. By stinging first the horses and then the coachman on his nose—she'll get that coach's wheels going round again—and round and round she buzzes, filled with her own importance.

At last the coach sets off again, with everybody walking—except the fly, who'd settled on the harness. The horses pulled, and up sprang that busybody of a fly now buzzing twice as loud, flying here and there, like a sergeant urging on his weary men to just one more charge—to victory!

The fly loudly complained that only she is doing the work and carries all the burden of the day.

After tremendous efforts by the horses, the coach at last reached the top of the pass.

'Phew!', said the fly, 'I'm quite worn out with all that work. Now, my good people, what about some recompense for all my trouble? But for me you'd never have reached the top!'

We all know people like that fly, people who must meddle in everybody's business. When bothered by such nuisances, chase them away or else your work will never get done.

THE HARE AND THE FROGS

In the cool, shady green of his home, a hare lay thinking, and the more he thought the more depressed he grew. He grew fretful and fearful and sadly thought: 'People like me who've so little courage find life very hard—they've no peace of mind to enjoy their lives, and never relax. We're ready to run at the slightest sound. My sleep is troubled and often I lie wide awake for hours at a time. Wise friends all say: "Get a grip on yourself and don't worry so!" What little they know!'

And as he thought, the hare grew sadder still. But it didn't do him any good for he was just as jumpy as before. A puff of wind, a passing shadow, the slightest sound—or none—made him start up in panic.

So the hare went for a walk in his melancholy way and thought: 'But can't my fear be overcome? I'm even ready to believe that men are just as scared as I sometimes!'

Suddenly, he heard a rustle close behind. Without a second's hesitation he bounded back towards his home, along the quickest route, around the shoreline of the lake.

The sound of his bounding and leaping made hundreds of frogs jump into the lake in fright.

'Can this be true!' exclaimed the hare. 'Does my appearance really startle others so? It's just as though I were a tiger! Well, it means one thing at least—however far I'm down the scale, there's always someone lower still!'

THE TORTOISE AND THE HARE

It's no good running late—one has to leave on time, and there's the story of the tortoise and the hare to prove my point.

'Let's have a bet,' said Mrs Tortoise to the hare. 'I'll beat you in a race to that old post on the hill.'

'You can't be serious,' said the hare, whose speed was legendary. 'Dear Mrs Tortoise, and I mean no disrespect, I think you'd better have a cup of good strong tea to clear your thoughts!'

'Thank you,' said Mrs Tortoise, 'my head's quite clear, and I repeat my challenge.'

The hare accepted and the race took place at once. I don't know what the prize was, nor the judge, but I think it must have been Judge Mole with his black and yellow cap.

The hare saw that he'd cover all the course in only four of his great leaps and seeing how little time he'd need, he just sat down and chewed a blade of grass. Time he'd lots of so he listened to the breeze sighing through the trees and smiled at the old tortoise with her plodding gait. His reputation for superior speed made it a point of honour he'd start late, so feeling hungry, he had a meal and after that he dozed and then he played at any game that took his fancy.

But quite by chance he looked towards the finishing post and saw that Mrs Tortoise was very nearly there. Although he bounded away to catch her up, she passed the post in front of him.

'There!' she cried, 'I was right after all—now where are you? For all your speed, you're second, and have lost the race! And what a handicap I laboured under, too! I've had to drag this heavy shell with me. Just think what you'd have done if you'd been lumbered with a ton of bricks across your back as well!'

THE HARE'S LONG EARS

Some animal armed with sharp horns had jabbed the King of Beasts, the mighty Lion, and filled with anger at this treacherous attack upon his person he banished from his kingdom all animals with horns.

A tiny hare, whose long ears cast great shadows on the ground feared the royal messengers would say those ears were horns. They wouldn't spare him—or his ears—if he were caught!

'Farewell, friend cricket,' he said sadly. 'I'm off as well. They'll say my ears are horns—you'll see!'

'What nonsense!' cried his even smaller friend. 'You must be mad—they're only ears and couldn't hurt a fly!'

'I can't run risks,' the hare said tearfully. 'I'm sure some nasty person will insist they're horns, they're both so very long and—well, they *look* like horns!'

He packed his simple gear and humped it on his back.

'It's no good, cricket, I must go—however hard I might protest, they'd not believe me, saying I was pleading like a lunatic—and they'd do more than lock me up!'

THE LION AND THE RAT

We should always try to help each other if we can.
You never know when you might need assistance
from someone humbler than yourself. This truth
I'll demonstrate with two short Fables (*).

From out beneath a lion's huge paws, a rat
emerged in fear, but quite unharmed. For once, the
King of Beasts showed magnanimity and let the rat
go free. This act of clemency was not to be forgotten
by the grateful rat. Now, who would think a lion
would be so friendly to so small a creature?

One day the lion was caught in a trapper's nets.
He roared like thunder, making the forest shake for
miles and he fought like—a lion!—to get free. But
the more he struggled the more entangled he
became.

The rat heard the noise and ran to the scene.
Small though he was, the patient rat wasted no time
in pointless fury. He bit at the ropes with knife-sharp
teeth until the lion was free.

(*) And for the other see *The Dove and the Ant*
(page 94). Though these are smaller animals, it's
true, it's only a matter of degree, and the moral's the
same for both these two.

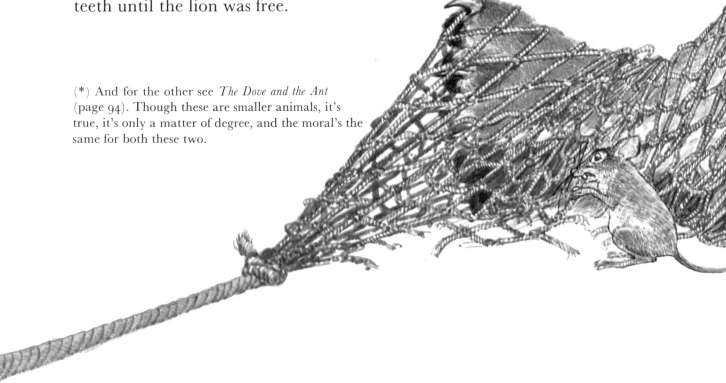

THE LION AND THE GNAT

'Buzz off, you beastly little insect, you curse of Nature,' roared the lion one day to the gnat.

The gnat was furious at being so insulted and cried:

'You may be called the King of Beasts, but that doesn't mean you've got a right to call me names. Your title doesn't frighten me—the ox is bigger than you but I can drive him wild with rage.'

The gnat resolved to teach the lion a lesson, and buzzing twice as loud as usual, flew round the lion and chose a moment to swoop down on his great neck to sting with all his force.

The lion stamped in pain and rage and roared his anger. For miles around the animals dived for their holes or bolted—and to think this general panic was all caused by one small, angry gnat!

He buzzed round and round selecting a new spot to sting. He stung the lion's jaw, then his tail, then his paws, and his back, Then he flew to his nose and stung him there as well.

The lion twisted and turned and stamped and roared and slashed with his sword, but his tiny foe just winged all round and laughed to see the lion slapping his neck, and his flanks and dancing about in fury and pain. He whacked himself so hard he actually drew his own blood, took great swipes at empty air and finally, worn out with effort, sank down in a state of near despair.

The triumphant gnat buzzed up and away, covered in glory, shouting her victory.

It dashed here and there, telling the tale

of the battle's ebb and flow, but became so excited it
didn't look out and flew right into a spider's web . . .

There are lessons galore to be drawn from all this,
but two are enough—first, one can't judge a foe
by size alone and next, while you'll dodge some
dangers so obviously great, watch out for the silent
and sinister ones that wait!

THE LION GROWN OLD

The Lion, the terror of the forests, now burdened with his years, mourning the loss of his great strength, was finally too weak to beat away attacks on him from his old subjects. As he grew weaker, they all grew bolder still.

The horse lashed out at him with well-directed hoof, the wolf nipped him with razor teeth, the ox came up and butted him with his long horns. They all took their revenge.

The sad, sick, weary lion had scarcely strength
to roar and waited for his fate without complaint.
Until he saw the donkey coming, then he groaned:
'Though I must go, since that's what Fate's
decreed, insults from donkeys mean a shameful
death indeed!'

63

THE LION AND THE DONKEY GO HUNTING

To celebrate his birthday, the King of Beasts decided on a Royal Hunt. Now, lions don't waste their time in chasing sparrows. They go for bigger, fiercer game, like boars and antlered stags. He'd use the donkey as his beater, since his raucous bray, far noisier than a huntsman's horn, would shake the forest.

Camouflaged with branches and festooned with leaves, the donkey was then posted in a thicket. The lion instructed him to bray when signalled and so drive all the animals for miles around into a panic. They, of course, weren't used to such a fearful din,

and when the donkey brayed, they all did as the lion
expected, bolting straight towards him.

'I played my part to great perfection, don't you
think?' the donkey said with pride.

'Indeed you did,' the lion replied. 'It was a dreadful
noise. If I didn't know you quite so well, I'd have
been frightened too, and taken to my heels!'

The donkey, had he dared, would have shown his
anger at this taunt, but he knew there was good reason
for the lion's teasing—no one can stand a donkey
bragging!

THE HEIFER, THE GOAT AND THE SHEEP IN PARTNERSHIP WITH THE LION

A heifer, a goat and a sheep made a pact with a
lion, and agreed to pool their profits and their
losses. One day the goat found a stag dead in her
trap and trotted off to tell her partners.

All came to see the prize and then the lion
counted on his fearsome claws like this:

'There are four of us to share this meat, so into
four I'll cut the carcase.'

When this was done, he claimed the first part, since he was the King.

'It's mine by right', he said. 'No one will gainsay that, I hope? As for the second part, I claim that's mine as well, since might is right, you know. As the most valiant of we four, the same goes for the third share. And now, a word of warning—let no one touch the fourth and last, or I'll lay claim to that as well—and eat the claimant, too!'

THE LION PREPARES FOR WAR

The lion had long been planning war and called a Council where each animal was allotted his military duties, each according to his capabilities.

The elephant's back would carry the artillery; the bear would carry out assaults up castle walls and over ramparts. The fox would use his cunning to confound the enemy.

The monkeys could be infantry, or when the need arose, distract the foe's attention by capering about.

Then a member of the Council said: 'I suggest we leave the donkeys out—they're slow and stupid. And the little hares—they're frightened of their very shadows!'

'No,' said the lion, 'I'll make good use of everyone. Without them all, our army would be incomplete. The donkey's bray will freeze the enemy's blood! As for the hares, their speed's just what we need for taking messages in the field.'

The lion was wise to draw the best from all his men. Each of their talents may help sway the outcome. Whether in peace or war, all have some part to play.

THE SICK LION AND THE FOXES

The King of Beasts one day fell sick and from his royal den summoned delegations from every different species to visit him and wish him well.

Official passes guaranteed their bearers strict immunity from laws of seizure, or even death from His Royal Majesty's teeth or claws.

But the foxes declined their sovereign's invitation, preferring to lie low in safety in their holes. What, asked the lion, was their reason for this lack of trust?

One of them saw that while the animals' tracks all pointed inwards to the lion's den, none pointed out again, to show they'd all safely emerged.

This so upset the foxes that they asked to be excused from joining in, for while they swore they did respect King Lion's good faith (and his official pass) they felt that though it might be easy to get in, it might not be so easy to get out again.

They wished him well from a safe distance, and stayed inside their holes despite His Majesty's insistence.

THE GUARD DOG AND THE WOLF

A wolf, a bag of bones, reduced to famine by the watchfulness of guard dogs, met a fine mastiff in the forest.

To kill him would have been a trifling matter in the ordinary way; but the wolf was weak and frail from hunger, and the mastiff would have beat him off with ease.

Instead, he humbly wished the splendid dog Good-day and praised his fine physique.

'Sir,' replied the dog, 'there's nothing to prevent you being well-fed. Leave your old forest, I beseech you.

Your brother wolves are just as starved as you. Silly fellows, sleeping rough, like frozen paupers. You'll die of hunger, mark my words, and Winter's not yet started! What an unstable life you have, never a good tuck-in with your own bowl, having to fight for every mouthful. Come back with me, and see how pleasant life can be!'

'What do I have to do?' the wolf enquired, licking his chops already.

'Oh, nothing much,' the mastiff said. 'Chase trespassers away and beggars, and wooden-legged sailors. Be pleasant to members of the household, but principally the master. And in return you get delicious food a-plenty, pickings of every sort, and juicy bones galore. And then what's more, they'll scratch your ears and stroke your back into the bargain!'

The wolf was overcome with deep emotion at such a prospect and tears came to his eyes.

But as they walked along, he saw that his friend's neck was sore and peeling.

'What has caused those marks?' he asked the mastiff.

'Oh, nothing—just a trifle—the chain pulls sometimes on my collar.'

'A chain!' exclaimed the wolf. 'You mean to tell me you're not free to run just where you please?'

'Not all the time, of course, but who minds that?'

'To me,' the wolf replied, 'it's so important I'll have none of your fine food and wine. I can't agree to terms like those even for a whole mine filled with gold.'

The wolf loped back to freedom, and as he ran he called back to the mastiff: 'Where there's a will there's a way to survive—goodbye!' and if he's any sense, he's running still!

THE FOX AND THE WOLF

I've often wondered why old Aesop credits foxes with more guile than wolves. Now, when the wolf is fighting for his life or trying to kill some other animal, isn't he as cunning as the fox? I thought he knew much more and might have said so, at risk of contradicting my respected master in the land of Fable. But I can't prove it, for here's a tale where all honour must be given to the fox.

One evening a fox spotted the moon's reflection at the bottom of a well—he assumed the rounded whiteness must be a luscious cheese.

Two buckets in the well went up and down alternately to bring up water. Our fox was as hungry as a wolf and didn't stop to think—he hopped into the bucket at the top. Under his weight, it shot to the bottom, while the empty one went to the top—and there they both stayed.

Now the fox was in a fix—he'd never get back to the top. How could he make his bucket rise again unless some other famished animal had just the same idea as he and used the other bucket to come down?

Two weary days went by and not a soul came near the well. The moon began to wane at last and lost its roundness, so that it looked as though a large piece had been bitten from it.

The fox was near despair, when who should come along but brother wolf, ever-hungry as he always was.

The fox called out: 'Friend wolf, I'll share a treat with you for once. You see this shining object by me? It's a splendid ripe old cheese made from the choicest cream. Why, even Jupiter himself would not disdain it. It would put life into the sickest man! I've only taken a small bite, as you can see. I'll give the rest to you with pleasure. You'll easily come down by getting in that empty bucket at the top.'

Now, wolves aren't often taken in by such unlikely tales but hunger proved much stronger than mere reason, so down he came. And, as he did so, the other bucket rose to the top and carried the fox to safety.

We ought not to poke fun at them, since we too build up theories on scarcely any evidence, just like that pair. We're all too eager to believe we see reality when it really isn't there.

THE WOLF AND THE STORK

Wolves are gluttons: very greedy. One
was eating in such a hurry he choked on
a bone. He was sure he'd die if someone
didn't come along at once and pull it out.
It was just as well for him that that
someone was the stork and since the wolf
could hardly say a word, he had to point
and growl and wave at her.

Down his throat she peered, saw what
the trouble was, and then with care,
tugging here and easing there, she pulled
the bone out from his throat.

Then—wouldn't you?—she asked him
for her fee.

'Your fee!' exclaimed the wolf. 'You're
joking, my good woman! Isn't it enough
to know your neck's safe from my savage
jaws. How ungrateful storks can be—
don't ever let me catch you in my paws!'

THE LAMB AND THE WOLF

Might always has the best of reasons for being right.

To show you what I mean let me tell you the story of the lamb who went to drink one sunny morning from a little stream.

A hungry wolf (they're always hungry) saw her there and growled:

'Who are you to dare to drink from my own stream? Speak up or I'll eat you at once!'

'Your Majesty,' quaked the lamb, 'please don't be angry. I was far below your part of the stream

and only drank a little, and quite a long way down. I couldn't spoil it, Sire!'

'But you have,' growled the wolf, licking his lips, 'and what's more, last year you made some sharp remarks about us wolves.'

'Sire, I'm much too young. This is the only time I've strayed from my flock.'

'Pah!' exclaimed the wolf, 'well, if it wasn't you, it was your brother.'

'But Sire, I haven't any brothers.'

'Then it was one of your miserable flock, they're always saying nasty things about us wolves, as though we hadn't troubles enough with your shepherds and your sheepdogs! I want vengeance—' and he sprang at the lamb and carried it into the heart of the forest there to eat it without bothering to find any more reasons.

THE WOLVES AND THE SHEEP

After more than a thousand years of strife the wolves agreed to make peace with the sheep, and all at last would be for the best between the two. If a wolf forgot the pact and slaughtered some stray sheep the shepherds wouldn't rest until they'd killed him in return, and every other one they could as well.

So the pact of peace was signed. To make quite sure it would be kept each side gave hostages, the wolves their cubs, the sheep their dogs.

The exchange was carried out with strict formality, watched over by the elders on both sides.

But then, as time went by, the cubs grew to full size and became what Nature intended they should be—big, heavy, savage wolves, hungry for blood and ready to embark on their carnivorous careers.

They laid a plot and chose a moment when the shepherds were away, killing as many of the lambs as they could reach, and fled into the forests.

Their elders, who were all still wolves at heart, forgot the pact as well and plotted with their cubs, killing all the sheepdogs as they slept. It was all so quickly done, not one escaped.

What good was it to sign a pact with wolves? Peace pacts themselves are frail enough, even between trustworthy people, but who'd believe the word of a wolf?

THE TWO PIGEONS

Two gentle pigeons lived at peace upon their private tree, but one of them grew restless for adventure and the wider world. This new idea became a passion and he packed his bags for a lengthy trip to distant lands.

The other said: 'What will you do for money? And why leave this pleasant place, and all our friends? Your absence will be felt by everyone, you know, though you don't seem to think of that. The only hope we have is that the hardships of travel, and dangers and troubles, will make you change your mind quite soon. If only it was Spring—why can't you wait until the warmer days are here? What's all the hurry? Only today, a raven croaked over the fate of some poor bird who'd disappeared. And I'll be worried all the time in case you've fallen in a trap or been pounced on by hawks. I'll be thinking: "Here's the rain again—I wonder if my brother is all right? I'll bet he hasn't got enough to eat, stuck in some frightful place that's cold and dangerous!"'

This speech helped make our would-be traveller still more depressed, but curiosity and his desire for change were far too strong. He answered: 'It's no good—I promise I'll be back within three days at most. Then I'll be satisfied. You'll see. I'll tell you all about my wonderful adventures. They'll cheer you up. And anyway, new sights, new sounds will give us lots to talk about, instead of just the same old daily round—I'll set the scenes of my adventures so exactly you'll feel you had been there as well.'

So they duly said goodbye and our adventurous pigeon flew off into the sky. A storm blew up and he was forced to dive for shelter to the nearest tree but it didn't give much cover since the Winter had already stripped its leaves away. He got completely soaked and lost a lot of his determination. But when the storm had passed, he started off again, trying to dry his soggy feathers as he walked along. He couldn't

fly with them like that. Then, in a field he saw a pile of yellow corn, and being so hungry didn't stop to think—he ran up to the pile and fell straight into nets that were spread across the bait.

Luckily for him, the nets were old and worn, and frantically the pigeon tore the cords, using beak and feet and even wings, still damp and soggy. At last he tore himself away, losing a few more feathers in the struggle. But just as he emerged, trailing bits of net around his neck, a vulture spotted him and swooped towards this half-dead convict who'd escaped.

Just then, a hawk flew by and while the two rapacious birds turned their attentions on each other, the pigeon fled, flying not much better than a lump of lead and landed on the roof of an old house. Here surely his terrible adventures would be over. But a nasty little boy (who'd learn respect for Nature in the end) loosed off his catapult at him and almost killed the pigeon. He escaped again, but only just in time, cursing his adventurous ideas. Half-dead, trailing one leg and both his wings, he crawled back home at last, keeping away from open roads and the world's aggressive denizens. And so our friends were reunited. How glad they were to be together once again you can imagine!

THE EAGLE, THE SOW AND THE CAT

The eagle watched over her nestlings at the top of a tree. At the foot lived a sow with her litter of piglets and between them, half way up, a cat and her kittens. All went about their lives in peace, until one day the cat upset this calm, well-ordered scene.

She climbed to the top, to the eagle's nest and said:

'Death will surely be our fate, or at least that of our children, which is almost the same thing, if something isn't done. You see how that old sow down there roots round the tree, digging away day after day? Eventually, she means to bring it crashing down, and then she'll pounce on all our little ones and eat them up. I might have time to rescue one of my dear kittens—I'd be thankful to be left with even one!'

The eagle was frightened enough, but the cat's plans weren't finished yet. Down she climbed to the ground and said to Mrs Sow: 'My good friend and

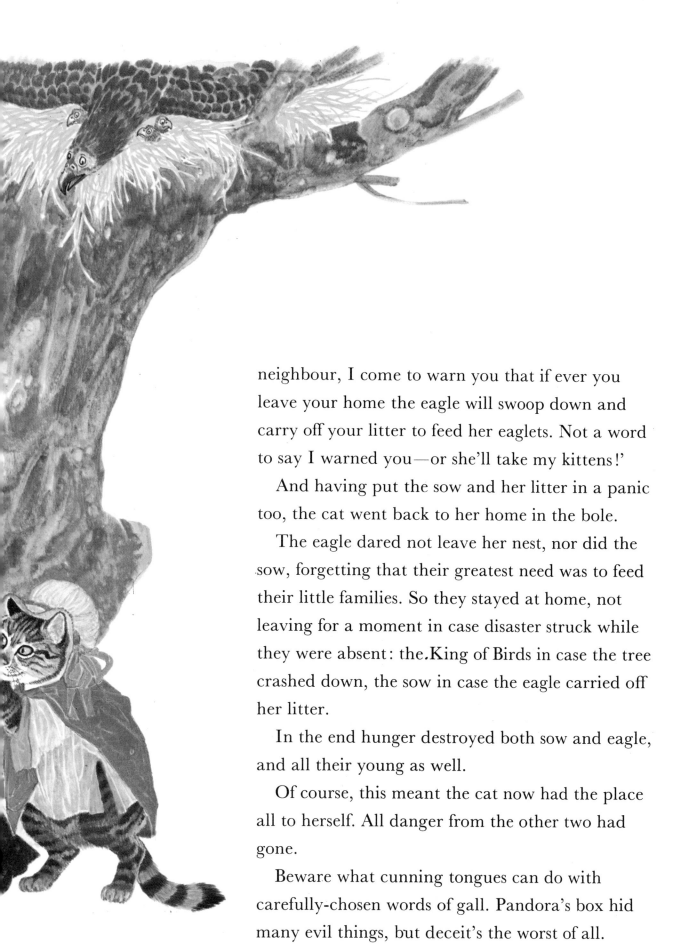

neighbour, I come to warn you that if ever you leave your home the eagle will swoop down and carry off your litter to feed her eaglets. Not a word to say I warned you—or she'll take my kittens!'

And having put the sow and her litter in a panic too, the cat went back to her home in the bole.

The eagle dared not leave her nest, nor did the sow, forgetting that their greatest need was to feed their little families. So they stayed at home, not leaving for a moment in case disaster struck while they were absent: the King of Birds in case the tree crashed down, the sow in case the eagle carried off her litter.

In the end hunger destroyed both sow and eagle, and all their young as well.

Of course, this meant the cat now had the place all to herself. All danger from the other two had gone.

Beware what cunning tongues can do with carefully-chosen words of gall. Pandora's box hid many evil things, but deceit's the worst of all.

THE OWL AND THE EAGLE

The owl and the eagle agreed to stop fighting each other and swore eternal friendship on their words as Birds. And never would they eat each other's little ones again, they promised.

'But do you know what mine look like?' the owl enquired.

'No,' said the eagle. 'I've never troubled to distinguish properly—I've never had the time!'

'Ah, well,' the owl said sadly, 'then it's no use—they're as good as dead already. If I come back and find them in the nest, it's only luck that will have saved them. As you're the royal and kingly bird among us, you'll not be one to stop and think before you eat them up. Whatever wise owls say, I say that Kings and Gods lump everything that looks alike together—it's farewell to my nurslings if you find my nest.'

'I promise I'll not touch them,' swore the eagle. 'Show them to me, or at least describe them fully.'

'Ah, my little ones are beautiful, well-made, so sweet, far prettier than any other little bird. You'll distinguish them at once from my description. Please don't forget—remember what I've said.'

Later that year the owl produced a nest of little owls and soon after that event the eagle was out hunting and saw, quite by chance, in a cleft in the rock, or it may have been, I can't remember which, the crumbling roof of some old church, a clutch of horrid little monsters, sour-faced, sad-eyed, and screeching all out loud.

'These little horrors aren't the children of my friend the owl,' the eagle thought. 'I'll eat the lot . . .', and he swallowed them all. When eagles dine, there's not much left, and when the owl returned, only her children's claws remained.

The owl wailed loudly in complaint and called on all the gods to witness her distress.

One of them leaned down from a cloud and sadly replied:

'The fault is yours, dear Mrs Owl, or rather it's a fault that's common to all parents when they boast their offspring are well-made and handsome, beautiful and happy reproductions of themselves. That's how you lovingly described them to the royal bird. Now, come, you must admit, your description was absurd!'

THE JAY DISGUISED IN PEACOCKS' FEATHERS

The peacocks were moulting. A jay flew by and gathered up their cast-off plumage, carefully arranging it around him.

Then, off he went to strut among them, convinced he was as elegant as any there.

But he was recognised at last. The angry peacocks flew at him and tore his stolen finery off—and much of his own plumage too—and chased him from their garden.

He fled for safety to his brother jays, but they disdained him, too.

We've plenty of two-legged human jays who swagger round our city streets in cast-off plumage. To say they're copy-cats is letting them off lightly —I think 'impersonators' would be more accurate and fair.

Well, I won't say any more—it isn't my affair.

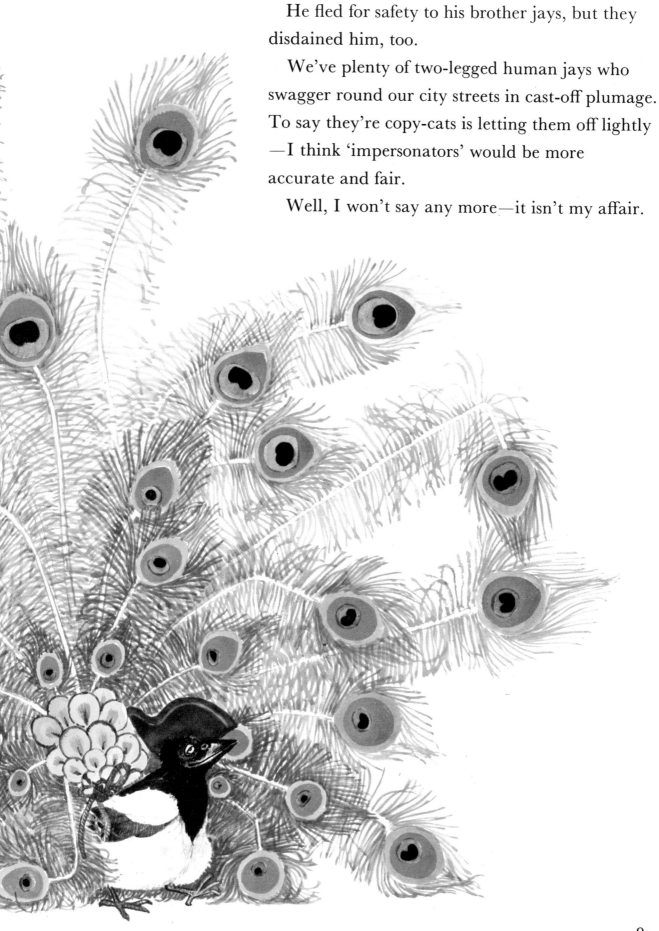

THE TORTOISE AND THE DUCKS

With her usual daily round, old Mrs Tortoise was really very bored, and she longed to see new sights and distant lands. The farther fields seem always greener, and those with meagre imaginations crave such grand experiences.

Two friendly ducks she knew heard her ideas and cried that they could help her to achieve her life's ambition.

'You see that long horizon, that wide sky? It leads to the vast plains of Asia and the Indian strand. We'll take you with us if you like. You'll see a dozen lands, broad oceans, distant kingdoms, strange peoples, and bring back a hundred stories of their ways of life.'

The tortoise pondered their suggestion, and agreed. The ducks then fashioned a short stick from an old branch, and in the centre made the tortoise grip it firmly with her teeth.

'Now keep tight hold,' they said. 'Don't open your mouth whatever you do, not even to sneeze!'

One at each end, the ducks took hold and slowly bore old Mrs Tortoise high in the sky.

On the fast-receding ground below a crowd soon gathered staring upwards in amazement at the sight of Mrs Tortoise suspended on a stick between the ducks.

'Come quickly!' they called to each other. 'Come and see the Queen of all the Tortoises flying with her escorts to the clouds!'

The tortoise quite forgot the ducks' instructions, opened her mouth and cried:

'Yes, your Queen I am indeed—stop your mocking shouts or I'll be much displeased!'

She would have done far better to keep her mouth tight shut but since she didn't and forgot her dizzy height, the stick dropped from her teeth, and down she went, down to her death below among the gaping crowds, the victim of sheer vanity, imprudence and idle curiosity, faults which inevitably forced

her swift descent.
Born to her wingless state, she
should have stayed content.

89

THE KITE AND THE NIGHTINGALE

The kite, a murderous villain, spread fear throughout the district. Even the children had to throw stones at him to keep him from their pets.

In baffled rage, he fell upon a luckless nightingale. This tiny herald of the Spring pleaded for her life by singing:

'I wouldn't be a tasty meal for you at all—hardly a mouthful—I'm a songster and all tiny bones. Listen rather to my singing till some better meal comes by—I'll sing to you of Tereus of old—'

'Tereus, you say? Is that dish worthy of a hungry kite?'

'No, he was a King of Athens, long ago. I'll tell his story, and mine too, and how we met—I know it will enchant you—my singing is the envy of the world.'

The brutal kite wasn't impressed, and croaked:

'Now then, what is all this about? I'm famished and you sing to me about old Kings and things—'

'But Kings wait on my words!' cried the little bird.

'Well, if a King had caught you, that would be the time for singing. As for a hungry kite like me, I'm stone-deaf to your pleading!'

THE HERON

An elegant, long-legged heron delicately picked his way along the bank, neck slightly inclined to watch the slowly-moving water, translucent in the sun.

His sharp eyes saw the carp, fat fellows all, and then a pike or two. The heron could so easily have picked them out and eaten all he wanted.

But he felt he'd wait until some choicer dish appeared and cultivate a fiercer appetite meanwhile. Meal-times were meant to be respected and it wasn't time to eat in earnest yet.

The heron came a little closer to the edge and saw some tench, oblivious of his shadow.

But tench weren't to his taste. He'd wait a little longer, and show how finicky an eater was the heron.

'I'll not insult my stomach with such stuff—what would my good friends say!'

The tench swam safely past, followed by some even smaller gudgeon.

'Gudgeon! Why, this worse than ever,' cried the heron. 'I wouldn't deign to open my long beak to taste such rubbish.'

But he was going to be obliged to open it for less. The fish had now all gone, the river flowed by clear and empty and My Lord Heron was fast becoming ravenous. At last, he saw a snail and decided not to criticize this lowly dish. He promptly ate it and was thankful to assuage his appetite with such a humble bite.

Those who most easily adapt to circumstances spare themselves a lot of trouble. Trying for too much quite often means you lose all you might gain. Never disdain the simplest offering.

THE CROW WHO TRIED TO BE AN EAGLE

A famished crow stalked by and watched an eagle lift away a sheep in his strong talons. Now, while the crow was weak compared to such a royal bird, his hunger was as great.

He'd do the same—he'd seize a sheep as well.

Round the flock he flew, looking for the fattest, finest sheep among them. He'd not be satisfied with less than best. At last, he saw the one he wanted—a meal fit for a King. His bright, black eye considered it from every angle.

'I can't look up your pedigree, but judging by your aspect, my fine sheep, your pedigree must be magnificent—you'll do me very well!'

On to the sheep's broad back he flew (though, as you see, it was a ram) and tried to pick it up. It was so heavy that it never even moved, and what was worse, his claws got tangled in the sheep's thick, hairy wool. The more he struggled to get free, the more entangled he became and since he couldn't lift the sheep, the only thing to do was abandon the attempt. But he was now too late. Up ran the shepherd with a cage and clapped him in it, where he sits croaking to this day, unless some kindly person has released him at long last.

But if that crow could speak, here's what he'd say:

'Stick to what you know and don't go imitating others. Example sometimes leads even the wise astray, so where a powerful wasp might smash his way out of a spider's web, a feeble gnat won't have the strength to get away.'

THE DOVE AND THE ANT

A dove was drinking from a sparkling stream when suddenly a tiny ant fell in close by. In such a sea of water, the ant was lost and struggled in a hopeless panic to regain the bank.

The dove quickly threw a blade of grass into the water. The ant climbed on to it and floated back to safety.

The tiny creature scurried off just as a hungry yokel came along, armed with a wicked-looking crossbow. He saw the dove still drinking from the stream.

The yokel grinned and carefully took aim—

The watching ant chose just that moment to sting him on the heel.

The man sprang round, the noise alarmed the dove, who flew away to safety in the trees, and with it disappeared our yokel's tasty meal!

THE BEAR AND THE TWO HOPEFULS

Two friends, hard-pressed for ready cash, sold the skin of a
bear they hadn't yet shot to their neighbour, a furrier.
They'd have the skin along quite soon, they said. It was,
they swore, the biggest bear he'd ever see (when they
brought it back, of course, but that would be quite soon).
It was wearing such a pelt the furrier would be made a
wealthy man—he'd surely split it up into a dozen coats.

They guaranteed to bring it back in just a couple of days.
The bargain struck, the money paid, the hopeful pair set off
at once.

They found the bear—or rather, he found them, and
charged at once. The two stood petrified. Faced with its
challenge, they quite forgot their contract with the furrier.
The first intrepid huntsman shinned quickly up a tree, and
the other one fell flat, down on his face, and pretended to
be dead. (He'd read somewhere that bears don't care for
corpses, they'd rather have fresh meat than some old carcase).

The bear (he must have read the same thing too!) saw
the body laid out flat, and sure it must be dead, prepared to
leave the scene but just to make quite sure came up and
turned it over, sniffing for some signs of life.

'Not a flicker,' said the bear, 'not a breath left in its body
—I'm off. My, how it smells already!' And back he trotted
to the forest.

The huntsman who had climbed the tree slid to the
ground and ran to his companion, who still faked dead, too
terrified to move.

'What luck!' the first one cried, 'but what about our
deal? We've got the money, but no hide! And by the way,
what did old Bruin whisper in your ear? He came quite

close, and even turned you sideways with his paws.'

'I'll tell you what he said,' cried his friend, sitting up at last, still quaking. 'He said: "Next time, wait till you're sure—no good selling Bruin's hide until you've pegged it out upon the floor!" '

THE BEAR AND THE MAN WHO LOVED GARDENS

In a thick and gloomy stretch of forest, an old and
grumpy bear lived all alone, entirely hidden from his
fellows. Solitude, however, was getting on his nerves.
It isn't natural to live entirely on one's own. It's good to
talk to others sometimes, even to be silent in some
friendly company; though talk and silence both are bad
when it's all of one and none of the other.

No other animal dared venture through the bear's
domain, which stayed deserted save for him, and bearish
though he was, it saddened him to see he had no friends.
While he brooded on his fate, close by, unknown to him,
there lived an ancient gardener in similar state.

He loved his garden and was expert on each bush and
plant and tree. It's a wonderful way of passing time,
and useful too, but plants and trees don't talk and he
longed for much less silent company.

Dissatisfied with silent things our gardener set off one
sunny day to seek some other soul of similar tastes.

The bear, who'd had the very same idea, had come
down from his forest home and at a turning by a hedge
they met, both equally astonished by the other's
presence.

The gardener jumped with fright—how could he get
away? Running would be useless, so he stuck his ground
and bade the bear 'Good Morning!' with no show of
fear.

The bear, never a brilliant talker, just growled:
'Tea at my den.' The gardener bowed, but as he
much preferred his own place to some gloomy den, said:

'Good Sir Bear, from here you see my little home—I should be honoured if you'd come and have a simple meal with me instead. There is fruit I grow myself and honey from my hives. Perhaps these aren't the things that persons of such high estate as you would eat in the ordinary way, but you'd be very welcome just the same.'

The bear was very touched by this and off they went, the best of friends before they even reached the gardener's house. They got on well so fast that Bear and Gardener stayed together and, since solitude is better shared, even with a bear, they settled down without a qualm.

The bear said little, not being one for idle chatter and the gardener could garden by the hour in peace. The bear went hunting for their meat and saw their pot was filled with richest stews and did his share of household chores. And when the sun struck hot he stayed at home and chased the flies away from his friend's face.

But tragedy was close. One day, the gardener lay asleep stretched on his back against the rockery. A buzzing horse-fly settled on his nose. The bear waved it away but back it came again. 'I'll get it,' swore the bear, 'I know a thing or two!' The bear pulled up a rock and hurled it at the fly. Granted, he killed the fly —and his poor friend as well! His aim was good, but the reasoning was faulty.

The one-time gardener now lay as still as stone. Nothing is worse than a foolish friend. Better have a clever enemy—or live alone!

THE ANGLER AND THE LITTLE FISH

Little fish may grow to be much bigger fish, so long
as their luck holds. To drop them back because they're
small isn't a policy that's clever, for if you let them
go they may be gone for ever.

A tiny carp, no bigger than your thumb, was
hooked up by an angler from a stream.

'Well, every little helps' the angler sighed,
considering his tiny catch. 'Here's the beginning of a
meal at any rate—let's pop it in the basket.'

The carp wriggled and squeaked: 'What good am
I to you? Hardly a single mouthful. But if you throw
me back again I'll grow ten times the size, and on
your hook for sure I'll fall one day. Then you'll
have a fish worth eating. But if you take me now,
you'll have to catch a hundred more just like me, too,
and even then we shan't make up a single dish for
one. So why waste time on me?'

'I won't, then,' said the angler. 'Your reasoning is
good but my immediate need for food is greater
still—into my bag you go!'

A fish on the hook is worth two in the stream—at
least when you've caught it you're sure of a meal.
You may never catch any others at all no matter
how brilliant your scheme.

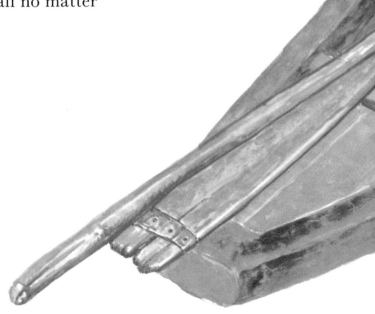

THE FISHES AND THE CORMORANT

This wise old cormorant had fished in every lake for miles around, in reservoirs and fish-ponds too. Sooner or later, all had yielded him a meal.

But he grew old and somewhat frail. His nourishment declined as well and since he needed strength to feed himself, the outlook steadily grew bleaker. Even his piercing sight began to fail and having neither net nor hook like human fishermen hunger began to bite as he grew weaker.

But cormorants are wise old birds, and since Necessity is the mother of Invention, he soon hit upon a trick. A crab basked on the lakeside in the sun.

'Madam!' cried the cormorant, 'please go and tell the fishes hereabouts that they're all doomed—the owner of this lake is going to drag it thoroughly with nets and every fish will perish!'

The crab ran off to tell the fishes, causing great alarm. They all assembled by the shore at once to seek the latest news from him and cried: 'Good Doctor Cormorant, what shall we do? Where did you hear this dreadul news? What can you do to help us?'

'The answer's simple,' said the cormorant, 'move from the lake at once.'

'But how could we do that? We have no wings like you!'

'Then you can borrow mine—I'll carry you, each one, to a wide and secret lake I know, not far from here, where you'll be safe as any fish can be. No

human fishermen know of it; it's only known to me
and God. It's in a spot Dame Nature wrought
with her own hands, safe from all treachery.
Life can begin anew for all of you.'

The fishes were all very pleased to hear this
marvellous news, and one by one they let the
cormorant carry them away to his wide and secret
lake—which wasn't wide at all, being clear and
shallow and altogether very narrow.

And when he'd flown them from the lake, he found
he'd stocked his larder for many a year. Day by day
he ate them at his leisure. The lesson they all learned
too late was never to place your trust in those
whose task in life is to dispose of others.

106

TOWN MOUSE AND COUNTRY MOUSE

The town mouse sent an invitation to his distant country cousin to dinner in the bright lights of the city.

Our two mice dined in state. Thick Turkey carpets were laid upon the floor and the dishes were superb and very tasty. Nothing was forgotten and they both tucked in.

But then their feast was silenced in a panic.

Outside their door they heard a noise. Both dived for cover in a flash.

The noise decreased, the footsteps died away. The country mouse decided it was time to go. His city friend protested: 'Come on, let's finish up our meal!'

'No fear!' the country mouse retorted, adjusting hat and gloves. 'Tomorrow you shall dine with me. Please don't infer from this that I disdained your meal—it was delicious, but . . . in my secluded little home I needn't leap for cover at every passing stranger. I'll see you at my house tomorrow night where dinner won't be interrupted by unwelcome danger!'

THE RAT AND THE ELEPHANT

A very small rat was not a bit impressed by a giant of
an elephant, as big as a ship. It found much amusement
in its slow gait, the swaying construction on its back
and especially the numbers of its crew.

It was on a pilgrimage, taking its master, a famous
Sultan (I forget his name) plus all his dogs, his cat,
and monkey too, his parrot, his old mother, all his
household, crammed into the flimsy shack upon its back.

The rat confessed himself astonished that the crowds
along the route were so concerned with size alone,
as if mere size had merit.

'What do you see to marvel at, you humans? Is it the
girth of its great body? If so, you ought to know that
rats, small though they are, are just as good as any
elephant!'

The rat was warming to his theme when suddenly
the Sultan's cat leapt from its basket and demonstrated
in a flash that rats aren't quite the same as elephants!

THE RATS CALL A MEETING

One cat was so intensely feared by rats throughout the district you hardly ever saw one, even in the dark. He'd killed so many, the few remaining didn't dare to leave their holes, growing weak with hunger.

This cat was no mere house cat, but a tiger, and the danger was that soon there'd be no rats to carry on— the race of rats would then be but a memory.

One peaceful day he was away, getting married so they say, and during the lull the rats all met to plan their next step in the war. The eldest rat (being a cautious and experienced rat, he'd stayed alive quite long!) spoke last and said it was his view that sooner and not later they'd have to string a bell around its neck, so when the cat went hunting, everyone would hear him coming and have time to get away.

There was, he stressed, no other way. The meeting quite agreed that nothing could be simpler to decide.

Then came the little matter of the bell and who should have the task of tying it round his neck.

One said: 'Not me—I'm not as stupid as I look!'

Another said: 'I wouldn't know how to begin—or how I'd end!'

Nothing was done and the meeting soon broke up. I've seen—and you will too—lots of such pointless conclaves, mere talk which ended without action. Calling a meeting's easy, and it seethes with bright ideas that aren't subject to doubt. But when it's time for braves to volunteer—there's not a soul about!

THE RAT AND THE OYSTER

A rat grew tired of his daily round and having not much commonsense decided on a voyage of discovery. He left his fields, his grain and his safe hole and tramped away across the countryside. In twenty minutes' walk he'd done a thousand miles—or so he thought.

'How big the world is,' he exclaimed, 'that range of mountains must surely be the Alps, and over there I see the Caucasus.'

The smallest molehill was at least a mountain to his simple brain.

After a few days' journey, our seasoned traveller came down to the sea where on a quiet and peaceful shore a host of oysters lay dozing in the heat.

'These must be ships of war,' he thought, 'of which I've read so much. What a pity my old father wasn't an adventurous explorer too. He hated travelling and always found a reason not to stray. As for his son— that's me—I've now seen all the oceans, and struggled, parched with thirst, through hot and trackless deserts!'

He'd picked up these racy and descriptive phrases from his teachers, and quoted them whenever he felt brave, not being a rat who chewed right through whole books and so amassed a wealth of useful knowledge.

Among so many closed and sleepy oysters, he was surprised to find just one with open hatch, yawning wide into the breeze, and all at ease with innocent repose.

It was round and fat and glistening, and surely of exquisite taste. The rat went sniffing round and smiled: 'I see this ship has food aboard, and judging by the smell of it, I'll certainly eat well.'

The rat stretched out his neck to reach into the oyster's shell, but just as he was going to sink his teeth into the dish, the hatch snapped shut, and he was trapped.

If your experience of the world is small, it pays to stay in port, and wait till you've been taught, or else like our friend rat, into a similar trap you'll very likely fall.

THE FOX AND THE STORK

The fox invited Mrs Stork to dine with him. The meal was meagre, just a shallow plate of broth. Our friend the fox was not a one for wasting money and the stork, though famished, couldn't scoop a mouthful up with her unwieldy beak. As for the fox, he'd finished in a moment.

Storks aren't vindictive birds, it isn't in their nature, but this particular prank she felt she should repay.

A little later, the fox was bidden to her house to lunch. This invitation he accepted saying: 'How nice not to be bound by useless ceremony—I never am—that's what good friends are for!' and at the appointed time he trotted into Mrs Stork's, all eager for the meal.

They wished each other hearty appetites and sniffed the heavenly smell of roasted duck, a dish the fox quite doted on.

But Mrs Stork had served the pieces at the bottom of a long-necked vase and while her slender beak could reach the meat, our fox's muzzle was too big—and anyway too short!

He had to leave the luscious dish and having eaten nothing, slunk back in silence to his hole, ashamed at being outsmarted so.

I've written this for cheats to read, so let this be a lesson to you all not to exceed the bounds of civilized behaviour!

THE FOX AND THE GRAPES

There was a fox from Gascony (some say he's
Norman-born) who saw a bunch of juicy grapes,
just out of reach, glistening in the morning sun.

These would be just the thing to quell his aching
hunger, and his thirst as well, but he couldn't reach
the vines, try as he might.

'Pah!' he snapped. 'They're green, I see, and only
fit for soldiery, or pressing cheaper wines!'

Let's end for all time the unwarrantable slur that
will insist the fox is no philosopher!

THE FOX AND THE CROW

The crow, a well-dressed thief, stopped on a tree to taste his latest booty, a ripe and smelly cheese.

The fox came trotting by, and hailed the crow:

'Why, if it isn't Mr Crow. You're looking very spruce and smart! And your fine voice, so I've heard tell, is finer than your plumage.'

These flattering words puffed up the crow with pride and resolving to demonstrate his marvellous voice, he opened his beak—and dropped the cheese.

'Most generous crow, you ought by now to know that flatterers live on the empty-heads they praise so freely. I hope you'll think this lesson worth a good, ripe cheese!'

The laughing fox picked up the cheese and trotted off to eat it in seclusion in his den.

The crow was silent, stung with shame, and vowed (though rather late) he'd not so easily be caught again.

THE FOX WHO LOST HIS TAIL

A master of cunning, a sly old fox, was finally caught in a trap, a cruel old-fashioned spring that clashed its iron jaws. It was a narrow shave. He was unhurt, but had to leave behind his fine, long brush, his tail.

Furious, and more than ashamed of his appearance, he resolved to use his cunning to convince his pack that being without a tail was best.

At the next meeting of the foxes' council he demanded:

'What use are tails? They should be lopped off now— then we could run as fast as any hound.

'This idea we'll certainly look into,' they agreed. 'But before we take such drastic steps, turn round and let us see . . .'

The fox did as they asked. The sight raised such a din of laughter and derision that the tailless fox at once sat down and said no more.

Long tails on foxes to this day is still the law.

THE FOX, THE WOLF AND THE HORSE

One young fox (for all his youthful looks, quite cunning), saw his first horse and to a friendly wolf came running with the news.

'Come and look: there's a nice, big animal grazing in our fields. Its size is most impressive.'

'Is it stronger than the two of us,?' laughed the wolf. 'Describe him, my young friend.'

'Were I a painter or a student of animal form I'd soon depict it, and whet your appetite with loving and colourful description. But come yourself instead and see—it may well be some new prey that Nature and good luck have sent us.'

'Good sir,' the fox cried heartily, heading the horse off, 'we'd much appreciate your name, for we've not met.'

The horse, who wasn't quite so stupid as he looked, replied: 'You'll see my name imprinted round my hoof—the smith does that each time I'm shod, and so can tell his handiwork.'

The fox said he was sorry that he couldn't read: 'My ancestors weren't keen on education. Always too poor, they could only just afford to feed us all, with nothing left for lessons. But the wolf is, luckily, well-versed.'

Flattered by such praise, the wolf came close to read the name supposedly engraved around the horse's hoof, but vanity was going to cost him four of his most valuable teeth.

The horse lashed out and promptly galloped off. Down went the wolf, his jaw quite out of joint. The fox said quickly to the furious wolf:

'I see this unnamed animal has left his mark upon your jaws —your inspection of his hoof does rather emphasize what learned friends so often tell me—that the wise must treat what's new with circumspection!'

THE FOX AND THE GOAT

Captain Fox (long since retired from army life, though he enjoyed the title) was strolling through the country with his long-horned friend, the goat.

This animal was none too clever, the end of his long nose being just about as far as he could see, while Captain Fox was never at a loss.

Becoming thirsty they clambered down a well and drank the fresh, cool water greedily. Thirst quenched at last, they discovered getting out couldn't be so easily achieved.

'Now,' said the fox, 'what do we do? Drinking is all very well, but there isn't only that to life—we must get out of here. Ah, I have the answer—stand on your hind legs, good friend, and place your front ones up against the wall. Stretch out your lengthy neck, as much as possible. Then I'll climb up to the tips of your horns and so get out—and pull you after me!'

'By my goat's beard,' the other said, 'that *is* a good idea. I like clear-headed people such as you, who never panic, or give up and drown, but think things out with admirable logic. As for me, I'd never have thought of such a clever scheme!'

The fox climbed out and left his friend still down the well. It was too good an opportunity to miss for preaching lessons at the goat's expense. He extolled the virtues of being patient till other rescuers came by.

'Had Nature given you foresight as long as your goat's beard, you'd not so lightly climb into a well like this without seeing some way out of it again. Farewell, I'm off, and now it's up to you to find a way out too, so spare no efforts, goat. I'm sorry that I can't remain with you and help but I've got urgent business to attend to now I'm free!'

Whatever enterprise you undertake, be sure to visualize where it may lead, and you'll avoid a similar mistake.

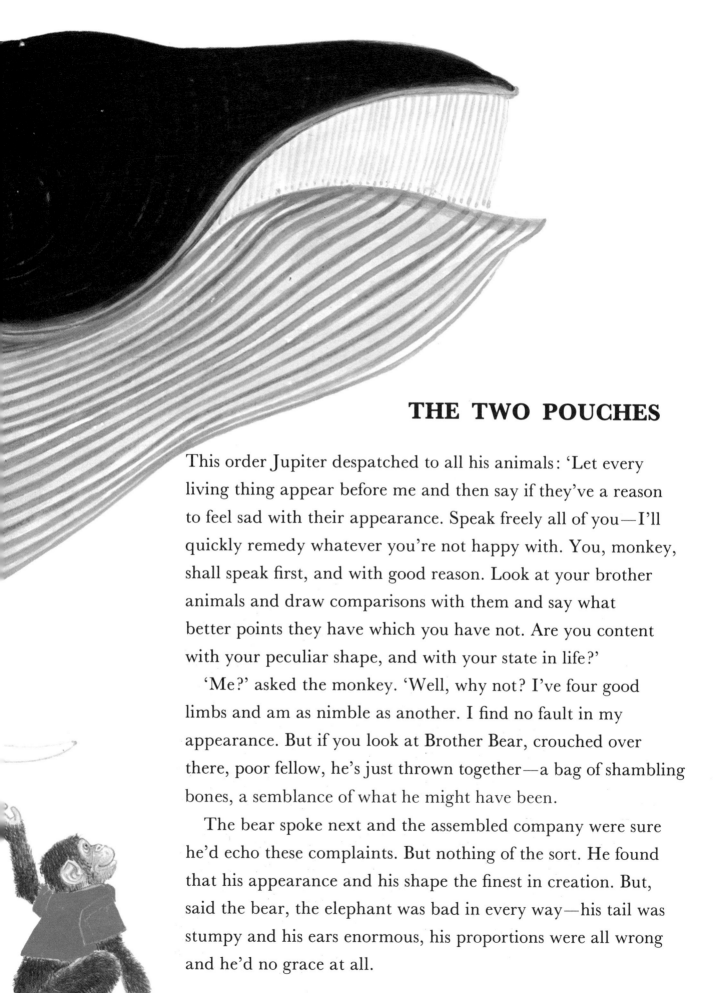

THE TWO POUCHES

This order Jupiter despatched to all his animals: 'Let every living thing appear before me and then say if they've a reason to feel sad with their appearance. Speak freely all of you—I'll quickly remedy whatever you're not happy with. You, monkey, shall speak first, and with good reason. Look at your brother animals and draw comparisons with them and say what better points they have which you have not. Are you content with your peculiar shape, and with your state in life?'

'Me?' asked the monkey. 'Well, why not? I've four good limbs and am as nimble as another. I find no fault in my appearance. But if you look at Brother Bear, crouched over there, poor fellow, he's just thrown together—a bag of shambling bones, a semblance of what he might have been.

The bear spoke next and the assembled company were sure he'd echo these complaints. But nothing of the sort. He found that his appearance and his shape the finest in creation. But, said the bear, the elephant was bad in every way—his tail was stumpy and his ears enormous, his proportions were all wrong and he'd no grace at all.

123

The elephant spoke next and wise though he was, he criticized the girth of Mrs Whale who, in his view, was far too fat and big and floppy. And so the talk went on, ending with Mrs Ant who said the mite was undersized compared with her, and that she was perfectly content.

Jupiter heard them all out, then sent them back about their lives again, happy that his animals were so content with their allotted states.

But when we look at Man, that foolish exhibitionist, he's the champion of them all and cannot be so easily dismissed.

With the faults of others we're as sharp-eyed as the lynx, but to our own we are as blind as moles. Our Creator gave us each two pouches: one that contains our faults we stow behind us out of sight, securely hidden from our foes. But we keep the faults of others in a pouch that's out in front and freely bring these out, to shout about them on the slightest provocation.

THE MONKEY, THE CHESTNUTS AND THE CAT

A monkey and a cat shared the same master, and two more cunning animals you'd never see. The monkey stole, even from the cat, and as for the latter, he was more concerned with having twice as many dinners as with catching mice.

One evening, stretched out by the fire, the furry little thieves were watching master's chestnuts roasting in the coals. They'd eat the lot if they got half a chance, and schemed how they might get them out.

'Look,' said the monkey to the cat, 'here's your chance to show what talent's in your claws. Pull these chestnuts from the fire. If Nature'd given me the claws you have, I wouldn't leave a single one!'

The cat stretched out a velvet paw and flexed its claws still more, and quickly rolled aside one chestnut, then another and another after that.

The monkey shelled them and as quickly as the cat could roll them out, he ate them. The cat was so intent on reaching the chestnuts without scorching his fur he didn't notice there'd be none left for him. And when a servant came to get her master's chestnuts, all had gone. Only a pile of shells and a smell of singeing fur remained. Both animals then fled, the monkey chuckling at his antics, while the cat vowed never to be flattered again into such unrewarding tactics.

THE FARMER AND HIS SONS

Work well done is worth your trouble.

A wealthy farmer, old and tired, called his children round his bed and said:

'Never sell your legacy—this farm, these fields—which in our family have always been, and must remain. I'll tell you all a secret—treasure somewhere on our land lies hidden. I don't know where it is, so you must search through every part of every field when harvesting is over. Dig and dig again, turn the earth well everywhere, wherever we have ploughed before as well. And while you're at it, see that the fields are turned and ready for next season's planting too.'

The farmer died. His sons did as he said and dug up every yard of every field, then laid the earth and drained it when they'd done.

They did their work so well indeed that twelve months later all the fields gave twice their normal crop.

Of course, they found no treasure chests, but did agree their father had been wise— that work produces wealth under another guise.

THE HAY CART STUCK IN THE MUD

Far from help of any kind a hay cart stopped, well
stuck in mud. It happened in one of those accursed spots
where no one ever passes. Fate sometimes deals us
blows like this so Heaven help us from being stuck in
such deserted places.

The carter swore and pushed and heaved and swore
again—but nothing shifted it. So he fell to cursing
everyone and everything—the ruts, the mud, his
creaking cart, his weary horses, even himself. At last,
for want of any other course, he called on him whose
muscles could perhaps provide the force to haul them
out.

'Strong Hercules,' the carter cried, 'lend me a hand.
If your great back could shift the world, surely you can
help to lift my cart from this mud-spattered hole?'

And from the clouds above a voice replied:

'Hercules can only lend his arm to those who show
a bit of courage. Now—look for the stones which stop
the cart from moving. From each of the wheels pull
out the clay and pack those holes with stones in turn.
Clear out a track in front. Take up your pick and move
that boulder from your path. Fill up that other hole.
Now, have you done just what I said?'

'Yes, indeed I have' the carter said.

'Now crack your whip—and then you'll see.'

'It's a miracle—the cart is moving! Thank you,
Hercules!'

The god replied: 'Be thankful you've good horses,
and remember this—the gods help those who help
themselves.'

DISPUTE OVER AN OYSTER

Along a sandy shore two strollers saw an oyster
and pointed it out to each other. There, in front of
them it lay—but who had seen it first? One bent
to pick it up, but the other stopped him, and
remarked:

'One moment—we must first of all determine
who shall have it. I say the first who saw it has it.'

'Well, if that's the test,' the other said,
'then my keen sight was first to spot it.'

'Come now,' the first one said, 'my sight's as
good as yours!'

'That's possible,' the second stroller said,
'but there's no denying that it was I who sniffed
it first!'

While this dispute grew warmer still, along
the beach there came a lawyer's clerk and being
appealed to, opened the disputed oyster,
swallowed it, and handed half its shell to each
of them.

Having disposed of it with such finality, he
wagged a finger at them both and with a
learned air intoned:

'This case was very simple—the Court awards
you each a shell. There'll be no costs. May each
of you depart in peace!' Courteously, he tipped
his hat and left the scene.

When one considers what it costs to bring an
action, it's best to think three times before you
start. Our lawyer's clerk was relatively cheap—his
master's fee would be ten times as steep!

THE IRON POT AND THE CLAY POT

The iron pot suggested to his friend of many years that they should really take a journey in each other's company.

But the clay pot shook his head and said it wouldn't be wise of him to stray too far away from the safety of the chimney corner. He was so very fragile and the slightest shock to him could well prove fatal—he'd be shattered into fragments.

'Though, for you,' the clay pot said, 'it's a very different matter—you're made of iron and can venture anywhere.'

'Have no fear,' replied his friend. 'If we meet with any danger, I'll quickly get in front and so protect you.'

The clay pot then agreed, and off they went, the iron pot by his side.

Clippity-cloppity, rather shakily, on their three legs, down the rough road. Of course, they bumped into each other as they clopped along, and the clay pot got the worst of it. Before they'd gone a hundred yards, the iron pot lurched and banged against his friend— and shattered him to pieces.

From this we'd better learn to congregate with our own species or else we'll meet the clay pot's fate.

THE RICH MAN AND THE COBBLER

The cobbler sang all day and half the night. It was a scene of innocent delight and wonderful to hear. He tried new tunes and melodies in different keys, as happy as a child.

But his neighbour, being a wealthy man, slept little and sang not at all.

And should he finally get to sleep, around the hour of dawn, he was soon awakened by the early-rising cobbler, singing at his work.

The rich man groaned and cursed the Heavens for making it so easy to buy food and drink and yet so hard to purchase sleep and peace of mind.

One day he sent for the singing cobbler and asked:

'How much do you make each year?'

'Each year? Why, Sir, I've no idea. Accounts aren't my strong point. I'm just a cobbler, not a banker and never know from day to day. But this I know—all my small bills are paid and I'm never short of work.'

'Well, then each day—how much do you take each day?'

'It all depends—some days are good, some bad. And on official holidays, well, nothing do I make. The priest is always giving us new Saints, but every new one means another holiday—and so no work for me that day!'

The rich man laughed at this philosophy and said:

'Today, I'll make you a happier man—here's a present of one thousand pounds—take care of it—it may one day be useful!'

Never had the cobbler seen so much, nor thought so much existed. He ran to his shop and buried it deep in his cellar.

But with it he buried his peace of mind.

He sang no more. Silent was his little house and all his cheerfulness had gone. And from that moment on, sleep left him. Worry and mistrust now kept him company.

Each day he watched the world go by suspiciously. Each night the slightest sound made him start up—even his cat hunting for mice made him think someone was digging up his hoard.

Finally, he could stand no more of it. He went back to the rich man's house and said:

'I beg you, Sir, take back your gift, it's not for me to keep, and let me have my happy songs and my untroubled sleep!'

THE OAK AND THE REED

Said the oak one day to the reed:

'You have reason to curse Nature. Even a wren
for you is a terrible load to endure. The lightest
breeze which skims across the water forces you
to bow your head. But I stand like a rock against
the mightiest storms. For you each zephyr is a
gale, for me it's all the same. Now, were you
born beneath my leaves, which cover such an
area, you'd not be so exposed. I'd shield you from

the storm. And in the summer, my leaves would give you shade from the sun's fierce rays.'

The great tree sighed.

'But mostly you small reeds are all intent on rooting close to the windy marshes on the water's edge. Nature has not been kind to you at all.'

'Your compassion,' said the reed, 'springs from a noble heart. But we should not deceive ourselves. The strongest winds to me are less a danger than you think. I bend, but do not break. So far, you have stood firm against their frightful blasts and have resisted without cracking. But let us wait awhile.'

As he finished, from the far horizon, black with storm-clouds, roared the most terrible of winds, torn from the coldest North, and fell upon the scene.

The oak stood firm, the reed bent flat along the ground. The wind redoubled efforts and screamed with such a blast it uprooted the majestic oak, whose head once touched the clouds, whose roots once ran so deep beneath the hallowed ground.

THE MILKMAID AND HER CHURN

With a churn of milk on her head, Perette set off for the
Fair. It was carefully balanced, and set on a pad to
keep it straight. She strode along in the simplest shoes
to ease her path and as she hurried, she worked out
what she'd get for it.

The milk, when sold, would fetch—let's see:
one hundred eggs at least, which when hatched out
would multiply by three. 'It's all quite simple,' said she.
'I'll rear the chickens near the house. The fox may
think he's a match for me, but I'll not leave him many
to steal. At least I'll have enough to buy a pig. And
fattening him will not cost much in bran. I'll see that I
get value when I sell him. And then with what he'll
fetch, I'll get a cow, and then there'll be a calf as well!
I can just imagine it, skipping round the house!'

At such a prospect, Perette skipped as well. But she
quite forgot the churn. It fell, the milk ran out and
with it disappeared calf, cow, and pig and chickens too!

The milkmaid cried to see her fortune dissipated so
completely and turned for home, trying out excuses
which would prevent her husband's rage.

A play was based on this sad plot, though it's no
longer acted on the stage. Its title was *The Milk Pot*, and
the moral was that: crying's no use—the milk is spilt—
there's no excuse!

THE OLD MAN AND THE THREE LADS

An old man of eighty was planting a tree. Three local lads stood watching him. One said:

'If you were building something, we could understand it better, the results would show at once, but a tree will take a lifetime to mature. You must be in your dotage!'

'What is the use,' they asked him, 'of planting it at all? What will you get from it yourself? You may grow older still, but then why burden life with cares about a future that's not yours? You ought to ponder your past errors and take steps to right them while there's time, and leave the hopes and dreams to us, the young. We are the ones who'll make the future world.'

'It doesn't rest with you alone,' the old man said. 'None of the works of man are easily erected, nor do they last. The hand of fate has equal influence on your young lives, as well as mine. Our spans of life are each so short they're much the same. Who among us here shall be the last to gaze upon the vault of Heaven? Can you be sure you'll still be here from one moment to the next? My descendants will be glad of this tree's shade. Come now, would you deny the wisdom of the old in creating with their hands some pleasure for their future generations to enjoy? Even today, it gives me pleasure to consider what will be. I shall enjoy it still tomorrow, and maybe for some time to come. Many a sun may set on your young graves while mine may still remain undug!'

And as so often happens, the old man was right.

One of the three young men went into the army and was killed by a random shot, the second fell from a tree whose branches he was cutting back, and the last was drowned at sea in a gale.

The old man shed a tear for each of them, and on their tombstones he himself engraved this tale.

DEATH AND THE WOODCUTTER

Bowed beneath the weight of heavy logs and
stiff with age, the woodcutter was trudging slowly
back towards his humble home.

But the load became so heavy and he felt so tired
that he stopped and set it down, and thought:

'What kind of life is this? Sometimes no food
all day, hardly a moment's rest . . . I have my wife
and children to support, and then the soldiery come
pillaging, and after them the tax collectors . . .'

He felt he'd had enough of life.

'Come quickly, Death!' he cried.

Death came near at once and said: 'Why do you
call for me so soon?'

'Oh, my!' the cutter stammered, 'you came so
very quickly . . . it was really just to help me get
this load upon my back again!'

It may be true for some that Death cures
everything, but most of us prefer, instead of tamely
dying, to suffer and fight on against the heaviest
odds, and worse.

That's the privilege of Man in Nature and this
Universe.